A Tale of Two Elephants

Colin Beazley

FOUR BOYS BOOKS

First published in Great Britain in 2013

Copyright © Colin Beazley 2012

The moral right of Colin Beazley to be identified as
the author of this work has been asserted in
accordance with the Copyright, Design and Patents
Act, 1988

British Library Cataloguing-in-Publication Data
A CIP record for this title is available from the
British Library

ISBN 978-0-9571396-4-0

Published by
Four Boys Books
Heywood House
Chulmleigh
Devon
EX18 7QS

Whilst this book is a work of fiction most events
referred to are true. Resemblance in some
instances to actual people living or dead, or locales
is purely coincidental.

Tribute to the Artist

There have been many books written about the elephant and undoubtedly there will be many more in the future. Some will include photographs of these fantastic creatures; a few will feature drawings of these inspiring animals.

This book is different in that its pages not only reveal something of the real life of these amazing animals but also celebrates their character with illustrations, faithfully and sensitively crafted by my friend, Colin Allbrook. Colin is an artist of national repute, his work has earned him many prestigious awards including, The Daler Rowney Award, The Turner Water Colour Award and The Terence Cuneo Medal for Equestrian Art.

I am grateful to him for sharing his wonderful drawings with us all. I hope you enjoy his gift as much as I do and find pleasure, as well as something of a challenge, within the pages of my book.

'Nature's great masterpiece, an elephant, the only harmless great thing.'
                                John Donne (1572-1631)

ALSO BY COLIN BEAZLEY

One Day in June

Within the Mist

Introduction

For many who read this story their experience of these giant creatures has been limited to their appearance in a zoo, or perhaps in the past, a performance in a circus. I have been one of the more fortunate people to have seen elephants living in the wilds of East Africa. As I researched for this story I was increasingly amazed at these animals' intelligence, power and gentleness; but above all, their astonishingly strong, family bond. It is impossible not to like these magnificent giants that have the power to destroy us with a stroke of their trunk, or crush us underfoot.

The elephant tales as told are of course imaginary, but far from fiction, they are based faithfully on truth, real experiences and old tales, nearly as old as the wide savannas and lofty mountains themselves: tales from an earlier age written long before we were born to this earth. The truth tells of how these animals, the largest mammals that walk our earth, have been treated by man; the way in which they have worked and served us, entertained and performed for us. Human greed has driven us to hunt them for their tusks, valuing their ivory more than continuing to experience the living, breathing elephant: its smell, sounds, splendour, nobility, and of course, its stories.

I hope you will be as enthralled as I by the tale of these two elephants.

Colin Beazley, March 2013

Chapter 1

My tale begins a long, long time ago in a land far away across the wide Atlantic Ocean. My name is Furaha which means 'delight' in Swahili, the language of my African homeland. My Mama had plenty of time to choose the name because she had cared for me in her tummy for nearly two years before I was born. She chose my name in the hope that my years as a young female elephant would prove a true delight to her and the rest of our herd.

"It's a good name," Mama said, because as we both came out from the shady thicket where I had been born an hour earlier, I was wobbling on my legs so much that it caused the others in the herd to laugh with delight.

Our homeland is vast. There are thousands of square miles of sun-baked savannah, grassland stretching from the coast in the east to the green hills and mountains beyond in the west. This has been the only home my family and forbears have ever known. In the summer the temperature soars and we have to spend much of our time searching the valley plains for water. Often, in the distance, I see lines of slow-moving elephants, silently ambling along together, silhouetted against the dawn light, the old ones moving more slowly at the end as they search for new feeding grounds. Many stay up in the mountains where it is much cooler.

Herds of buffalo, wildebeest, giraffe, zebra, gazelle and rhinoceros roam freely on our land, as do the lion and cheetah. None are safe. For us elephants, apart from the killer sun, it is man that is our greatest danger.

When I was a baby calf and dwarfed by my Mama, I would nestle between her forelegs to drink her milk. She stood towering over me, being nearly twelve feet high and told me, "We are the largest animals on the plains, probably in the whole of Africa."

My sister, who had already lost the reddish hair on her back and head when I was born, was four years older than me.   Our grandmothers and aunts kept an eye on us when Mama was not around. Whenever I got up to mischief and was naughty they would scold me, nudging me with their trunks to keep me in order. I remember Father told us, "The best way to learn, little ones, is to explore."

My early years were fun, playing with my sister, my cousins and the other calves and learning how to use my trunk. It is a funny old thing really: it's my long, strong, bendy nose, and of course I breathe through it.   I can use it to smell with, to pick up things even as small as a berry and to grasp leaves, branches and bark and put them in my mouth to eat. When I was small I had to kneel down to lap up water with my tongue. It was very awkward, but now I am older I can use my trunk.
"That's why we have trunks, to stop our knees from wearing out!" Mama would often say. It is great for sucking up water to drink, squirting it into my mouth, and I can bathe, spraying my back like a shower.

I also learnt how to blow the dust and sand over myself to help stay cool and get rid of those irritating little creatures that clung to my body and bit and itched so.

"When you get older," my aunts would tell me, "you'll be able to hold a stick in your trunk so you can scratch yourself."

When something alarmed the herd we would all trumpet by snorting and bellowing down our trunks. My early attempts sounded more like squeaks – hardly scary! The males, the big bulls, some of whom were nearly sixty years of age, stayed apart from the rest of us. When they were alarmed their call was very deep and loud. Mama said, "They're noisy cowards, 'old boys' who are no good when it comes to a fight and that includes your father!" The old cow elephants were the fiercest. When we were in danger they would rush towards the threat trumpeting and growling with their heads down, their tusks lowered, swaying from side to side.

As soon as my milk tusks started to grow, long before my permanent tusks, I knew it was time to begin to look after myself, "to let go of my Mama's tail" as we say, although I would still enjoy her refreshing milk. She was always there for me, our bond still strong, but now she spent more time helping my aunts with their young ones.

The days would pass in play, pretend fights, chasing the white egrets that would ride on our backs and, of course, having mud fights in the waterholes. Sometimes, if the earth was white, we would come out of the waterholes looking like elephant spirits. Already I was too heavy to be able to jump but I could run – well, walk very fast – twenty miles an hour or more. My tusks proved ideal for levering off tree bark and digging up roots to eat, but what I really enjoyed was munching on fruit and grass. I was happy to do that all day and most of the night.

"Flap your ears," the older elephants told me, "it will help you keep cool," but the real trick was to stay out of the sun, shading under some thorn bushes or lofty acacia trees, or sheltering between the big cow elephants. Too much sun and my soft baggy skin would burn.

During the times of drought I used my tusks and trunk to dig into dry river beds in search of water. We needed to drink a lot each day, perhaps one-hundred-and-fifty litres or more, and when the land was very dry food could also be a problem, since we eat only plants to satisfy our ravenous appetites. I had now learnt to push over trees to reach their branches, but these were only small ones. It was not unusual for us to walk twenty miles from our feeding grounds before we eventually discovered water: that can make your legs really tired.

Chapter 2

It is said that every beast has at least one memory they will carry with them their entire life. It may be a memory that's cherished forever, or one, as with me, of something that you wished had never happened and could be forgotten.

The orange fireball of the sunset had succumbed to the black of nightfall and this eventually gave way to yet another glorious summer's day. It was a day when the sun came early to our land, its yellow ball of flame still low in the cool sky.

The savannah stretched far into the distance to where a blue haze shimmered over the plain. All was well; the branches of the trees rustled and the long thick grasses moved in the morning breeze like waves on a lake. Water bubbled and spilled from the earth refreshing the muddy hollows. Here grumpy old hippos rested in safety, almost completely submerged, digesting their feast from the night before. Herds of animals roamed and grazed undisturbed, basking in the sun. All was at peace.

But then men came to our valley, many men.

Men had come to our land before to learn of our ways. They had been conservationists and wanted to study our habits, what and how much we ate, how many there were of us, how far our wanderings took us, and if we destroyed the crops and huts of the farmers. When they had finished their work they killed some of our kin and those in neighbouring herds to help the rest of us survive! Our friends and family whom we loved had been slaughtered.

These men, though, were different; they had not come to observe us or the scenery. They had come for something else . . . our gleaming tusks. They came in a cloud of dust, driving wagons to our resting place; the white men among them had guns, the black men had machetes. The eldest cow in our herd, the matriarch, raised her trunk and as she bellowed thunderously the other mothers gathered the young in a circle around her. Over forty of us stood, heads swaying, growling and screaming as we faced the men to defend the herd. The youngest ones were pushed between the big beasts, hidden by clouds of dust stirred up by their restless shuffling.

As the men approached shots rang out through the bush. Some of the bigger cows broke free from the group and, with heads lowered, trunks raised and ears spread wide, threatened the men. The noise of the herd was deafening. More shots. The group broke ranks and three cows, including my Mama, trunks against their chests and ears back, surged headlong at the men. The ground shook as two of the mighty beasts fell dead. Elephants scattered in every direction in the confusion and mayhem that followed. I was carried along with the other beasts through the undergrowth and thicket in a bid to escape the killing. We fled that fearful place and didn't stop until we were certain the men no longer followed us.

In time it became increasingly apparent to me that my Mama was not with us. I hoped she had escaped and made off in another direction. For an hour or more the old cows cried out with deep rumbling growls from their throats. Other elephants that had wandered afar throughout the bush and plain echoed their sad song.

The next day we returned to that place, the place that smelt of death, and beheld the carnage. Several of our herd had fallen, victim to the white men's guns. Under one great beast a tribesmen lay still, every bit of life crushed from him. The sight caused us to give up a deep moan. Vultures circled high on the thermals overhead, then, as a squabbling mass, descended onto the bodies of our dead, ripping at their flesh. Hyenas skulking nearby made off at our arrival, squirming and barking.

Twisted and entwined in a thorn tree, away from the others, lay Mama. My heart stopped. The men bringing death with their guns had stolen her life forever. Her blood was spilt on the earth, her flesh torn, swollen and festering with flies. And her face was gone. The men's greed had cut deep into her head: her huge, yellow, ivory tusks, the colour of the sun, were no more, ripped out by the evil poachers to trade in their markets.

We stood, my sister and I, staring at our butchered Mama. Our grief and pain was almost more than we could bear. I placed my foot on her back, hoping she would wake, in a desperate attempt to save the most precious thing in my life. I didn't know how I could go on without her. Laying her trunk soothingly on my forehead, my sister consoled me, "Mama's spirit will still roam free in the vast wilderness of the plains. Our brave and courageous, beautiful Mama."

Nothing more was to be said or done. After many hours we left that place of death and, in the heat of the midday sun, walked thirty weary miles to new grounds where those men would not find us.

Soon the rains returned across the mountains. The sky burst bringing with it the 'storm chasers' – wildebeest, zebra, springbok and cheetah – and the grasslands were alive again. The sight of the first rains caused great excitement in our herd. Our low groaning and trumpeting brought replies from other herds far, far away across the savannah in celebration of new life. I remember that Mama had always said she could recognise the calls of each and every elephant.

I greatly missed the call of my Mama.

Grumpy old hippos wallowed in the thick, oozing mud of the waterhole, disturbed only when one of them shifted, barging others out of the way. Perched on their slimy backs birds fed on flies and scooped up small passing fish. As we approached the watering place, some of these beasts looked at us with their small, raised eyes protruding above the water, then, taking a deep breath, they snorted through their nostrils before sinking out of sight. A few gangly giraffes appeared on the opposite bank and, after cautiously looking about, splayed their front legs wide apart and lowered their exceedingly long necks so they could drink. I could see now why we had trunks!

Geese standing in the shallows stirred uneasily as a pair of hippos came out of the water onto the land to feed near them and guinea fowl danced about in excitement. In the late afternoon and early evening impala, zebras and warthogs drank at the waterhole nervously watched by resting storks. Our nights spent near the waterhole were full of noise and at times I found the din almost deafening.

The following days were spent in relative peace, troubled only by the loss of my Mama. More men came but this time they were not bad men. They were the native rangers who patrolled the savannah. They were looking for skins, meat and pieces of the ivory tusks that might be hidden close to the waterhole. Hunters would store their bounty there to gather later when no patrols were nearby. The rangers talked of the poachers and how sickened they felt when they saw the terrible suffering, death and destruction of innocent animals caused by such evil men.

"If only humans would curb their greed for money and ivory, the killing of elephants would end," the Chief Ranger cried.

Three of us young ones had lost our Mamas and it was evident to the rangers from our appearance that we were not doing well and were missing their milk. They decided to take us by truck to the Ranger Station where they guided us into small enclosures which were already home to other calves.

Many carefree days passed uneventfully. We spent them eating lush grass, young acacia branches and maize stalks, drinking bottled milk, playing in our daily mud baths and being scrubbed by the rangers. The nights were long and often sleepless for me. I was grieving the loss of my family and the chance to roam freely again for I knew that once men had sheltered and fed us we would never be able to return to the wild. One of the very young, abandoned calves became poorly and feeble and, after days of being cared for, it died in its carer's arms. I don't think it had ever really got to know its family and mother. We didn't know the young one well but it is in our nature to feel sorrow and ache for such loss.

The following day a huge bull elephant was led into the station, his bones showing through his sickly body. He had fallen victim to a poacher's trap. The snare had cut deep into his trunk and leg, ripping them open as he had struggled to get away. The wound was festering and looked riddled with maggots. The once proud beast now looked weak, ill and in great agony, exhausted from days of wandering the plains. For two weeks of cold, long nights, the beast would moan and rumble, telling of his pain. Carers brought food and water to him and attended to his trunk and leg but a lingering death overcame his will and ability to live. It seems as if we are all fighting a losing battle to survive: these are such sad and uncertain times.

Early one morning, before the sun rose, the station erupted in chaos. Behind the house where the men stayed a brilliant red glow lit the dark sky. Fire! Flames were raging through the savannah destroying all in their path. Mile upon mile of dry grassland and bush were ablaze, fuelling the inferno. I could hear the screams of animals as they fled through the nearby bush ahead of the fire. We were now increasingly uneasy, trapped in our small huts. The rangers were panicking, chasing about, shouting and calling on their radios, preparing for escape. We could now smell thick, choking smoke drifting on the air. Our trumpeting and stamping finally brought our carers who led us, one by one, to waiting trucks.

As the trucks rattled and bounced their way along the track to safety the first rays of the sun broke over the far horizon. My life was now about to dramatically change.

Chapter 3

We were temporarily housed in a paddock on the edge of a small town. One memorable day a white man visited us. This man brought with him money, many men and lorries with large containers, and for me, a new home far away from the wild country I knew and loved. He described it as, "A new life way across the ocean in America, and a new family . . . in a circus!"

I hated every minute of it. Billed as 'El Elefante Gigante, the largest animal that walks the earth', the audiences laughed with glee as I stood there, less than six feet tall, under the massive, white canopy of the Big Top. A man in a top hat, a bright red jacket and wearing black trousers would announce it was "Showtime", and with that a young woman, balancing on a white horse, entered the circus ring. She rode round in circles whilst a man swung from a rope high up at the top of the tent and all the time loud music played and bright lights shone on me. I was expected to perform tricks, like standing on my hind legs and holding my trunk high, but I had never had to do anything like that before, so my early performances in the ring

were with the clowns who played and danced around me. It was a new and very strange world to me, and one I didn't like.

My keeper, a Frenchman named Serge, had worked in another circus and tried to be kind to me but that made little difference. Unfortunately it was not his circus. The Circus Master would shout at him, telling him to make me work harder and be more entertaining for the audience. I was meant to pull in the paying crowds by being the so-called star act that would ensure a sell-out. On occasions the Circus Master would use a metal bull-hook to jab me hard in my shoulder, trying to make me perform. Before my keeper saw he'd rub dirt into the wound but it would be sore and bleed and sometimes it turned bad. A man like that shouldn't have animals.

My days were spent chained in a cramped, dirty enclosure. I had been used to walking miles across the savannah but now I got little exercise and began to get problems with my feet and legs. There were no other elephants to spend time with. My life had become a lonely round of deafening audiences, glaring lights and beatings at the hand of the Circus Master. I felt abandoned in a world in which I had no desire to stay. As

I fought back so they restrained me with tighter ropes and stronger chains: they said it was to break me.

With the passing of the years I grew taller and stronger. My tusk teeth had broken through and grown to quite a length, and my trunk was now nearly six feet long. At almost three tons I was becoming more than they could easily manage. At times, when audience numbers were low, I had my rations cut and was blamed for poor ticket sales. My nature had changed and I was becoming more restless and difficult. I was not only able to scare children, but also adults, and some of the circus people as well.

Whenever we visited a new city or town on our tour, posters would go up everywhere announcing, 'The Circus Comes to Town', and I would be billed as the star attraction. We all paraded down the main street and, on one such occasion when I was bored with everything, I decided to wander off, away from the march, and into the throngs of folk crowding the sidewalks. People screamed and ran away scared, fearful I would harm them. There were claims that it was not an accident and that I had turned wild and dangerous. The Circus Master was forced by officials in the city to do something about it. Some people even called for me to be killed.

A kindly man came to see me. I could tell he was someone who was close to animals as he seemed to hear and understand me. He spent time with me and took me for a walk, asking me, "How do you like the circus? Are you happy?"

I left him in no doubt about how I felt and I believed him to be a good man. Afterwards he took me with him to the Circus Master and told him what needed to be done.

"She is not a pet or a performing trickster. I know she cannot go back to Africa but she needs, nevertheless, to be part of a family, to have other elephants to spend time with so she does not feel abandoned. She also needs the space to exercise and roam." I could tell he was becoming emotional, I sensed it in his voice, but he continued to speak firmly to the Circus Master. "She must come with me to my home, to my wildlife sanctuary, where she can be with her own kind, find herself again and live out her days. If she stays here with the circus your problems will never end and they'll only get worse. You will risk not only the safety of your circus family but also the lives of others. She is unhappy here."

I don't know what words were then shared between them, or for that matter what money, but knowing my Circus Master as I did, I'm sure he had to be paid to let me go.

Once again, after so many years of despair, I was filled with new hope for my future. For far too long I had been fighting just to survive and had grown more and more tired with every passing year.

After an uncomfortable and rather noisy journey in a draughty lorry I finally arrived at the wildlife park. From the first moment I stepped off the lorry ramp and put my feet on solid ground, I could tell this was going to be so very different from what I had known in all my years at the circus. The rolling land reached as far as I could see or imagine, and further. There were few fences across this rich grassland which stretched in every direction, and a vast forest of lush, leafy trees extended way down one side of the parkland to an inviting, shimmering watering place bordered by bushes and mud.

At first the quietness was unnerving after my days at the circus but I soon began to feel safe and that feeling was wonderful. Apart from the team of men who travelled with me, the only others were the 'good man', who had saved me, and a woman. No staring faces, no taunting and screaming children or demanding adults, no prodding keepers or cruel Circus Master.

And then slowly I could hear it: it had been there all the time, the 'call of the wild'. Birds squawked from the treetops, then gave shrill whistles as more dipped and dived overhead. I even heard the rustle of leaves as branches bent and trees swayed in the freshening breeze.

As I was gently led through a small paddock into a wooden barn to take food, water and rest, I made out the distant trumpet of elephants way off across the park. I curled my trunk up tightly as I always did, with its tip inside my mouth to stop any ants crawling up it and, for the first time in ages, slept deeply for a full four hours.

The morning sun rose with the dawning of another day and a new chapter in my life. All seemed well with the world, but then there was the most almighty commotion outside. I rose from my bed and strolled out of the barn to discover what all the fuss was about. There, on the other side of the paddock's high, wire fence was a large bull elephant, thrashing his trunk back and forth across the ground and sending clouds of dust up into the air. This gigantic creature restlessly rolled his head from side to side as he shifted his weight from one leg to the other and swished his tail. He behaved like a beast with a troubled soul. I have learnt that there are few sights more disturbing and heart-stopping for a man than the sight of a giant bull tusker behaving in this way. He was introduced to me. "This is Jumbo. He's not from your homeland of Africa but a more distant land in Asia between India and China, a country called Thailand." The 'good man' spoke to me in a reassuring and comforting manner and led me to where the old bull was demonstrating. In a firm voice he called Jumbo, then turned to me and said, "He only wants to meet you; it's his way of saying 'hello'."

During that day more elephants came to my paddock and we touched trunks and snorted, grumbling and purring as we talked with one another. Over the weeks that followed I roamed with the herd and began to bond with my new family, little knowing that Jumbo and I would one day entwine trunks and stand together as friends. My spirits lifted.

Jumbo looked very different from the bulls from my family in the African savannah and even the more elusive bulls of the forests there. He appeared altogether smaller, and certainly his triangular ears weren't as big as ours. In between them, on the top of his head, his forehead was bulbous and domed, not flat like mine. He looked a bit strange. The smoother skin of his face had patches of different colours on it and he boasted a pair of chalk-white tusks which gleamed in the sunlight, as did his small brown eyes. His smooth trunk had just one finger at its tip, not like my two. But the strangest thing was his legs – well, one leg in particular. It looked different from the others, most peculiar.

The word amongst my fellow elephants was that he had turned wild, becoming uncontrollable and attacking his keeper, which is why he was brought here.

When Jumbo stood still for any length of time he had the slightly funny habit of resting his trunk on one of his enormous front top teeth – his magnificent tusk. He said when he was tired it felt heavy. Jumbo must have been pretty old because he had grown his sixth set of teeth, but he tried to kid the others he hadn't yet reached the age of forty. Hour after hour he would wander and browse the range of the park by himself, searching out food and drinking vast amounts of water, just like our bull elephants at home. In the early mornings and moonlit evenings he would sink and squelch in the waterhole and, while swimming, lift his trunk above the water so he could breathe through it. I had not seen this trick before.

My family had always been cautious when drinking from new waterholes – creeks and springs were safer. Bad men had been known to poison the waterholes to kill any animals that drank from them, but here all seemed safe and the men were good. We all lived together in peace and some of the bull elephants would follow our family, turning from their old ways of staying apart. The parkland was lush with vegetation and grazing which rolled away far into the distance. The cool water was plentiful and the weather proved kind, free from the killer sun. Here my ageing cousins and I, neither wild nor tame, wandered at will. This was a place of refuge where we could live the remainder of our days without fear and threats, screaming crowds and cruel taskmasters. It had not always been like that for many of us: each had a tale to tell of their early years and Jumbo's was the most remarkable of all tales.

Chapter 4

Jumbo grew up in the forests of north east Thailand, close to the border with Burma. There he discovered how the local people used elephants to strip the forestlands of their valuable timber. As a young calf he was taken from his mother and chained to posts by his ankles and beaten until he learnt to do what was wanted of him by his trainer – his mahout. To many people, what went on hidden away in the high, dense, teak forests was indeed a mystery, but as loggers inevitably made more roads through the forests, clearing vast areas of trees for timber, life changed for Jumbo.

The forests of his homeland were monsoon forests with rains coming at certain times of the year. The warmth of the sun would make the valleys and hills smoke as it lifted the rain mist. In the dry season the trees changed their colours and then lost their leaves. Jumbo's forefathers had roamed in this land. These gentle giants had nobly led armies to war. They had also been spectacularly decorated with bright robes, ornaments, strings of bells and colourful paint and then marched in religious processions to magnificent temples. But for Jumbo, his life was a continual labour of dragging tons of logs and carrying heavy loads along mountain trails. Although he was young the work was hard: each day his muscular trunk and legs became stronger. His soft cushioned feet helped him to be more surefooted as he carried loads along the uneven and slippery trails. Jumbo could pick up sounds from the ground through his feet from the village many, many miles away.

Jumbo was born in a forest camp to a mother who had once been wild, then trapped in one of man's deep pits. Fortunately, having been unhurt she was not taken for meat but trained for work. Other adult elephants that men had tamed were brought to the pit and, with ropes and harnesses, had pulled his mother out. He had never known his father, who had lived in the wild outside the camp, maybe across the border in the country of Burma.

As a youngster he remembered how newly captured elephants had been driven by thousands of men beating through the forests into large stockades, with fences made of tall, stout poles rammed into the ground and lashed together with thick ropes. The desperate beasts would fling themselves against the walls of the stockade, terrified, only to be forced back by the keepers' yells and flaming torches which lit up the overarching forest, creating frightening shapes. Baby calves were dragged from their mothers who were noosed and tied up, and if any big bulls had been caught but resisted the rope, they were savagely thrashed. In the commotion they would butt each other, frantically trying to escape, and the screams of families torn apart could be heard echoing around the forest camp late into the night. For Jumbo it was a nightmare.

Soon after this time his training began. First came the taming, which crushed any free spirit he had within him. He was roped and chained tightly between two tame elephants and schooled for several hours each day, the rope ties cutting his legs to the bare bones. Struggle as he might he could not free himself: his wounds just became worse and more painful. The men used their tame beasts to keep the captive elephants calm. It helped knowing that this brutal treatment would eventually end.

A wiry, bow-legged, nut-coloured man wearing only a towel loincloth and white, woven hat, proudly stood before him. This

was to be his keeper and trainer, his driver, or as they were called, his mahout. After studying Jumbo's eyes, head, back and legs, measuring him and generally watching how he behaved, Jumbo's training began. His mahout, a committed man, had walked with elephants from a very young age along the ancient trails etched into the high mountains, the same tracks that elephants had used for hundreds of years.

He was a fine man, one that Jumbo respected. He worked hard with Jumbo for many days, and as they spent more time together the prods from his mahout's goad pole, with its metal hook and tip, became fewer. Jumbo learnt to go, sit, raise his foreleg and hind leg, reverse, lie down, lower his head, trumpet, push, pull and offer his foreleg for his mahout to stand on and climb up. The bond between them became stronger, and in time the movement of his rider's body and feet behind Jumbo's ears instinctively told Jumbo what was wanted. Throughout it all his mahout never lost his temper with him.

The working day in the timber camps was long. As a young bull in the cool mountains, he would start early in the morning and labour six hours before the sun bore harshly down. He often worked with another similarly aged bull harnessed alongside so they could haul logs: loads of five tons or more. As he grew he learnt how to carry trees resting across his tusks and held in place with his trunk. He would load the trees onto lorries destined for the sawmills, nudging each into place with great accuracy. A hearty meal of bamboo and bark was his reward.

The nights in the mountain camps were full of noise. The mahouts would feast and sleep nearby around smouldering fires of dried elephant dung which burnt late into the dark, starry nights. If any elephants were restless their mahout would tighten their rope ties and tree anchors and sometimes gently sing to them. Jumbo knew this was the life his mother had known all those years before.

To Jumbo life was a complete mystery, a wondrous adventure, but just as Jumbo began to settle into this rigorous routine the wickedness of men brought upheaval once again. Tears came to the kindly brown eyes of this wise, old bull as he shared with me the terror of that one day in the forest that he would never forget.

"I had started out early that day along the mountain trails while the air was still fresh. I led two other elephants, comrades that I'd worked with before. When there was a break in the trees, distant mountain tops revealed themselves, shimmering in the sunlight. This was a land I had not ventured to before. I was now a fine, young tusker: intelligent, fast to learn, skilful and, above all, strong. My mahout and I had grown close and I was able to sense when my rider was uneasy, anxious or hesitant with his commands. Today's trek was just such a journey.

"That evening the mahouts made camp and tied ropes between the rear legs of each elephant to hobble us so we couldn't forage too far from where they cooked and slept by their fire. Something unsettled me and I listened hard with my spreading ears, but heard nothing. All seemed well, so I ventured into the forest in search of food. The other two elephants were some distance from me when there was an almighty blast and flash of light. I remembered feeling the ground shake beneath my feet and then swell up as my whole body collapsed under me. Metal flew about in all directions. As I screamed and writhed in agony, I could hear my mahout cry out to me, then there was another explosion a little way off."

Jumbo told me that they had climbed into an area of the country which was close to the border with its neighbour, Burma. Jumbo's wanderings, whilst hunting for food, had taken him across into the 'killing fields' of that land, the massive areas where soldiers and rebel fighters, at war with each other, had laid deadly landmines. These explosives patiently waited in secret until trodden on. Jumbo knew that such things existed; he had seen children and villagers hurt by mines. There had also been people fleeing from the fighting in that land and crossing into Jumbo's homeland, not along roads guarded and free of mines, but rather along the jungle and forest tracks. Many had been killed, blown apart or maimed.

"I rolled from side to side on the forest floor, senseless, my right front leg causing me great pain and bleeding badly. I trumpeted aloud again and again. Eventually one of the other mahouts came to me and very soon folk from the nearby village had gathered around. The mine had blown my foot away and some of my leg just below the knee. Whilst women tied cloth, leaves and vines around my leg, the men and mahouts brought two other elephants alongside me. They used thick ropes to hoist me onto my feet between the two bulls. The journey was long and slow; for the first part two men scouted ahead sweeping long bamboo canes from side to side before them, trying to detect any more unexploded mines.

"It took more than a day to descend the deep ravine and cross the river to the logging camp and, for me, hours of pain, feeling weaker with every step. Once at the encampment people worked hard on my leg. They gave me food that somehow helped take away some of the pain. I slept in the lengthening shadows of the mighty trees and when I woke my leg was wrapped tightly and the bleeding had finally stopped. I couldn't really feel it and I myself felt very strange and giddy; I couldn't help thinking that my leg looked shorter. I was too weak to stand so quietly lay resting but knowing that if I couldn't walk I would surely die. It was then that it occurred to me that I hadn't seen my mahout since the explosions."

Jumbo told me that the following day a group of farmers carried a wrapped body into the camp, bundled on a bamboo palate which hung from a long pole. They laid it down before a shrine and others gathered as they chanted in their own tongue. Jumbo continued to suffer with his leg and with the misery of not seeing his mahout again. He believed that the dead body was that of his lifelong man-friend who had given him his name.

After many days he was taken by truck to a reserve outside a large town. In this special place, lots of people worked on his bad leg.

When he woke this time, he found he had a new leg attached to him that was not his own; nor was it even a real leg. A kindly woman told him it was made of things called plastic, sawdust and metal!

"I knew what sawdust was but not the others. What I do remember is the great discomfort

and difficulty as I managed to wobble along on my own three legs and the other thing! I used my trunk to lean on to help support my injured leg. The woman told me that because I was healthy and strong I would survive."

Jumbo was still a young elephant and, as he grew taller and heavier, the kind men there made him a longer, stronger leg to support him, with toenails painted on it. These were the same men who had made many, many arms and legs for people who had lost them in landmine explosions, like he had.

He realised then that although his walking became easier he would never, ever be able to work again in the forest, moving trees. He didn't know what future awaited him now.

So it was that one day a different truck came to the reserve. Jumbo was loaded onto it for the start of the longest journey of his life. The smoky old vehicle trundled for mile after mile, hour after hour, along the rough, pot-holed roads that few others travelled, heading away from the forests and mountains into the fertile flatlands and on to where the sea began. When Jumbo got out of the truck, he saw many things he had never seen before; high, giant buildings that seemed to float on water, lots of water, as far as he could see. Something very long moved, hissing steam and then trumpeting, not unlike him, as it slowly disappeared out of sight. As he stood beside one of the big buildings many men gathered around him admiring his leg and telling him how lucky he had been.

From the dockside Jumbo was lifted in a strong canvas sling made like a hammock which passed under his tummy and was raised by a tall tower. He swung from side to side high above the ground feeling ill and very unsafe. Men below talked loudly, pointing at him and laughing. Finally he was lowered into the belly of the building, which he learnt was a ship, and so began the next part of his journey to a land called America. A bountiful supply of leaves and grasses, bananas, mangoes, corn and sugarcane was given him, along with fresh water and a block which tasted just like the salty rock of home. A comfortable bed had been made in the strange, dark surroundings for him.

Jumbo recalled, "The ship rolled violently and I suffered bad sickness in my stomach and when I tried to stand I felt very unsteady."

He spent many days and nights in the ship's belly with only a shaft of light falling from the sky above through a grid in the roof. During his journey many different men came to him and brought him water and food, but one old, weather-beaten man spent much time sitting close, whispering to him, feeding him and carting away his dung. The old boy often touched fire to a wooden stick in his mouth which bellowed sweet, scented smoke.

As Jumbo slept on that journey he remembered his life back home in the forest before he lost his leg, and feared what would happen to him now.

Chapter 5

His removal from the ship's belly was no more majestic than when he was lowered in, but at least he was back on solid ground. The journey that followed was in a much better and quieter truck and on smoother roads which were wider and full of other vehicles.

Jumbo's new home was a large, solid, brick building. Above its door was painted an elephant's head nearly as big as his own and the words, 'Elephant House'. Inside were several stalls and outside it opened onto a shady yard surrounded by a ditch and stone wall. He was to share the yard with another bull elephant that spent much of his time walking round and round in circles about a tree which grew in the centre of the yard. His new companion, Chandra, seemed odd to Jumbo at first, but as he got to know him they became close friends, fellow tuskers.

Chandra told Jumbo, "This is the second zoo I've lived in, and in this one men are much kinder than in the other. In the first zoo I was caged on my own in a small, bare, dark pen and that's why I think now I keep circling around. I was watched by screaming people who threw peanuts and coins at me: it was a cruel place."

Jumbo didn't know what peanuts and coins were but he certainly knew what living in a dark, ship's belly was like and what was meant by 'cruel'.

"To begin with I was terrified by the cries of creatures, big cats and hyenas in nearby cages, especially after dark, but I slowly got used to it," Chandra reassured Jumbo.

Each zoo day was much the same as the last. At their keeper's commands, 'get up' and 'go out', Jumbo had learnt from Chandra to rise from his rest and follow him out and down to the pool for exercise and water. Often they would be hosed down, and if their keeper put the hose on the ground they could pick it up with their trunks and use it to spray in their mouths. This would bring laughter from anybody who was watching. Their keeper always approached them slowly and in a manner not to startle them. Jumbo was not allowed to touch the keeper until he had first stroked Jumbo's trunk in the way of an elephant greeting. Their keeper was a seasoned and dedicated man who kept control of them both with his commands, and sometimes with a thump from an elephant hook.

For Jumbo some things were very different from life in the wild: on the command 'lift leg', his keeper would cut away part of the bottom of Jumbo's three feet and trim his toenails. If he called a command and struck Jumbo's new leg with the hook, Jumbo would gracefully lie down so his leg could be unstrapped, allowing him to sleep in comfort. During his time in the zoo Jumbo had two more legs made for him, each a bit bigger than the last.

Over time he learnt many new ways. He discovered how to paint on large boards with a long stick in his trunk; visitors to the zoo seemed amused at that, especially children. He gave rides to families who climbed up a wooden tower and clambered into a box, a howdah, which was mounted on his strong, curved back. The keeper walked him back and forth, up and down, on earth tracks between cages and folk would scream and giggle. They loved it. They adored the way he pulled up a root and banged it against his leg to shake off the earth. If it was hot, Jumbo would take the water hose his keeper had left on the ground and, when he wasn't looking, spray the keeper with water, much to the delight of the crowd. If his keeper approached him and lifted Jumbo's trunk to his face, Jumbo knew to blow and the keeper

would pretend to fall over backwards: the crowds clapped and cheered. Jumbo thought this was great fun.

All this time Chandra was becoming stranger and more distant from Jumbo, no longer talking to him in those sleep-sounds that are too deep for men to hear. Jumbo didn't think he looked so well and seemed lost. One day Chandra badly attacked their keeper, not 'backing up' when commanded to. He would have killed him if Jumbo had not driven Chandra away from the man as he escaped. Chained in his stall Chandra grew more and more violent. Jumbo couldn't understand what was wrong. Amongst the keepers there was talk of it being the old bull's age, and something to do with his 'musth', the smell he produced, which made him mad, uncontrollable and ready to attack people.

The chief zoo man came and visited the elephant house more often and once Jumbo heard him say, "Chandra has death in his eyes. The only thing we can do with him is to keep him tightly chained forever, or kill him."

Jumbo thought that the chief zoo man must have considered Chandra to be too dangerous to keep where there were people.

One day the old bull disappeared and was never seen again.

Jumbo was sad at the loss of his friend but he went on playing; he knew the people would always come there to see him. Children cried and laughed and came clutching small toy elephants which they showed him. But all this time, no matter how hard his keeper worked to spend time with him, Jumbo saw him less and less. The chief zoo man now had him looking after other animals in the zoo and ordered that Jumbo should spend more time chained in the elephant house. Jumbo was very sad.

"The crowds stopped coming to see me. I know my keeper realised how lonely I felt because I heard him tell the chief zoo man when they visited the now half-empty elephant house. He said, 'What Jumbo needs is the company of other elephants. It is cruel to keep him alone and if you will send him to live with other elephants I will stay and help look after the other animals in the zoo'."

And now, as an old bull roaming the open lands of the sanctuary, he had found something he had not known for a long while: companionship. His life had been memorable and full of surprises. He had no wish to try and escape but wanted to spend his last days bathing, drinking, eating hay and grain as well as foraging amongst the forest and grasslands. Life was easy. The seasons came and went and little changed, only the weather.

One spring day, early in the year, as the trees were filling with leaves and the cold had finally left this blessed place, we discovered Jumbo lying near the creek like a big bundle of bones. He was very ill. At times one of us would be unwell and a man would visit us and give us things to make us better. But this was different. Jumbo had been looking weaker and thinner for some weeks, taking himself away on his own more and more, and the man's visits had not seemed to help. The kindly man and woman who had brought me here spent each day with Jumbo in his barn, bringing him food. Jumbo must have decided early on this day, whilst it was still cool, to go down to the water and there he fell.

We elephants live for a very long while and Jumbo was more than sixty years old. His last set of teeth had grown many years earlier, and when we have no more teeth to come and can no longer chew our food, our long lives come to an end. That's how it had been for Jumbo. He would not walk down to the waterhole again. He had left his old body for good, and lives no longer in this world but in the next.

For much of that day we all stood over Jumbo, groaning and rumbling.

Chapter 6

During Jumbo's years at the zoo the people of the nearby town had grown very fond of him. The children loved his charming and comical ways and older folk adored his warm and gentle nature. Soon after Jumbo left the zoo, conditions got increasingly worse and some people came and campaigned to have it closed down.

There is now a small menagerie of farm animals where the zoo used to be. The children of the town love to visit and play there and, with their parents, look after the animals. The older generation of the town still cherish fond memories of Jumbo the elephant and, in his memory, have erected a grand statue of him outside his old home.

Above the large doors to the building, which have now been boarded up, it is just possible to make out the painting of an elephant's head as well as the words, 'Elephant House'. They know that in the last months Jumbo spent much of his time chained by his legs here or pacing around the tiny paddock. But they also know, and are grateful, that his last

ELEPHANT HOUSE

years at the sanctuary were happy and peaceful ones.

Below Jumbo's life-size statue, of him resting his trunk on one of his tusks, reads the inscription: 'We will never forget our very special friend whom we all love and miss so much, dear Jumbo'. The money the local town people raised for Jumbo's memorial was far more than was needed so with the rest they built a children's playground around Jumbo. The young children of the town now hear afresh about the story of their Jumbo and, on the first day of summer every year, people of all ages arrive at the park to celebrate Jumbo's birthday. He would have loved the cakes!

Whenever Furaha talked of Jumbo to other elephants, young or old, it filled her with pride that they had once been dear friends and it was nice to think they still were.

After Jumbo's passing she had to find herself again: who she was. She lived for seven more happy years. The younger elephants followed her around the park, grateful for her leadership and wisdom, and together they shared stories of their long lives, their adventures and losses. Old age finally caught up with her and there was no escaping it: Jumbo wanted her back. She too now would join all those noble elephants that had gone before, and together they would silently amble along some high and distant horizon, towards the setting, orange sun.

Jumbo and Furaha had finally come home.

Shortly before Furaha's passing, a woman from Africa was in America with her family on holiday. She visited the sanctuary where Furaha lived. Her children were so taken with Furaha and how content and happy she seemed that they made their father take lots of photographs of her. Years later that same woman was asked to draw an illustration of an African elephant and she rediscovered the photographs of Furaha.

So, that is how Furaha came to be regarded by many as the most memorable of African elephants, illustrated, as she was, on the front of the BENKI KUU YA TANZANIA – the Tanzanian 10,000 shillings banknote.

Just as we have become the elephant's enemy, so we are its hope, trying to save and protect us both in the future.

Our relationship with these awesome creatures goes back in history thousands of years. We need to remember that "The most meaningful thing about our history is what we learn from it".